CONQUERING TOXIC EMOTIONS

WORKBOOK & SELF-DISCOVERY JOURNAL

Rhonda Favano

ISBN: 978-0-9988534-5-1
Printed in the United States of America
First printing.

Growing Healthy Homes LLC
P.O. Box 3154
Bartlesville, OK 74006

To obtain additional copies of this book, please visit
www.GrowingHealthyHomes.com.

Disclaimer: The information presented in the book is for educational purposes only. It is not intended to diagnose, treat, cure, or prevent any disease or illness. If you have a medical condition, please consult the health care provider of your choice.

The author is not liable for the misuse or misunderstanding of any information contained within this publication.

After extensive research, the author has concluded that Young Living Essential Oils are 100% pure, authentic, and unadulterated. This is supported by their proprietary Seed to Seal® process. The author encourages you to do your own research and be an informed consumer.

I would like to thank Tammy Bennett for her contribution
and support in bringing my vision of this journal to fruition.

I created this workbook and guided self-discovery journal to enhance your journey through *Conquering Toxic Emotions.*

Our emotions, thoughts, and paradigms can keep us imprisoned and just beyond the life we desire and deserve. I applaud you for taking this first step toward getting off the roller coaster and transforming your life!!

Delving into our emotional muck can be a bit overwhelming, and this workbook is intended to further empower and equip you for a successful outcome. Most experiences outside of our comfort zone are unsettling, so I encourage you to commit to 30 days of self-discovery, self-improvement and inner healing as you forge ahead toward true emotional freedom.

TABLE OF CONTENTS

THE EMOTIONAL PHYSIOLOGY CONNECTION

Read Chapter 1, pp. 13-16 of *Conquering Toxic Emotions* before completing this section.

OILY SUGGESTIONS: Apply Stress Away™, Lavender or Peace & Calming® to pulse points, and inhale deeply.

Our unresolved emotional experiences are recorded in cellular memory (DNA) and remain there as live programming until they are dealt with. They are stored within our body until we address them so that they may be properly filed.

The three aspects that make humans multi-dimensional are:

1) ______________________________

2) ______________________________

3) ______________________________

How would you define emotions?______________________

____

____

Emotions may cause ________________ changes!

As you completed the exercise on page 15, recalling a time when you were really scared, what physical effects did you experience?

____

____

What are your earliest childhood memories?

List the emotions associated with those memories:

Of the emotions you listed above, which ones leave you feeling uncomfortable?

When you are ready to begin clearing toxic emotions, these emotions would be a great place for you to start.

Record any physical symptoms you experience when recalling those emotions:

NOTES, THOUGHTS, IDEAS:

WHAT IS ENERGY?

Read Chapter 2, pp. 17-21 of *Conquering Toxic Emotions* before completing this section.

OILY SUGGESTIONS: Apply Clarity™, Cedarwood or Vetiver to temples and brain stem, and inhale deeply.

How would you describe energy? ______________________

____

____

The Law of Vibration says everything that exists in the universe consists of pure energy, which resonates and exists as a vibratory frequency. *(Dooley, Mike, "The Law of Vibration," http://www.one-mind-one-energy.com/Law-of-vibration.html)*

All ____________, ____________and ____________ have energetic vibrations.

There are only two kinds of vibrations: positive and negative. Every mood or feeling causes you to emit, send-out or offer a vibration.

Our emotions are an internal guidance system.

List some of the emotions you have experienced in the last 24 hours.

____

____

Which of these emotions do you prefer to no longer experience?

____

____

When you walk into a room where there was recently an argument, you will feel the negative energy. Conversely, when there is harmony, you will feel the positive energy.

Energy Centers, also known as ___________, are the areas where energy ___________ through the body.

EKGs measure electrical activity of the ___________, and EEGs are used to detect the electrical activity of the ___________.

In her book, "Scriptural Essence, Temple Secrets Revealed", Janet McBride provides a biblical explanation of Chakras:
"The description of the Menorah is a mirror image of the ___________ electrical energy centers of the ___________ column, known as ___________."

The degree of openness and flow of ___________ through your ___________ determines your state of ___________ and ___________.

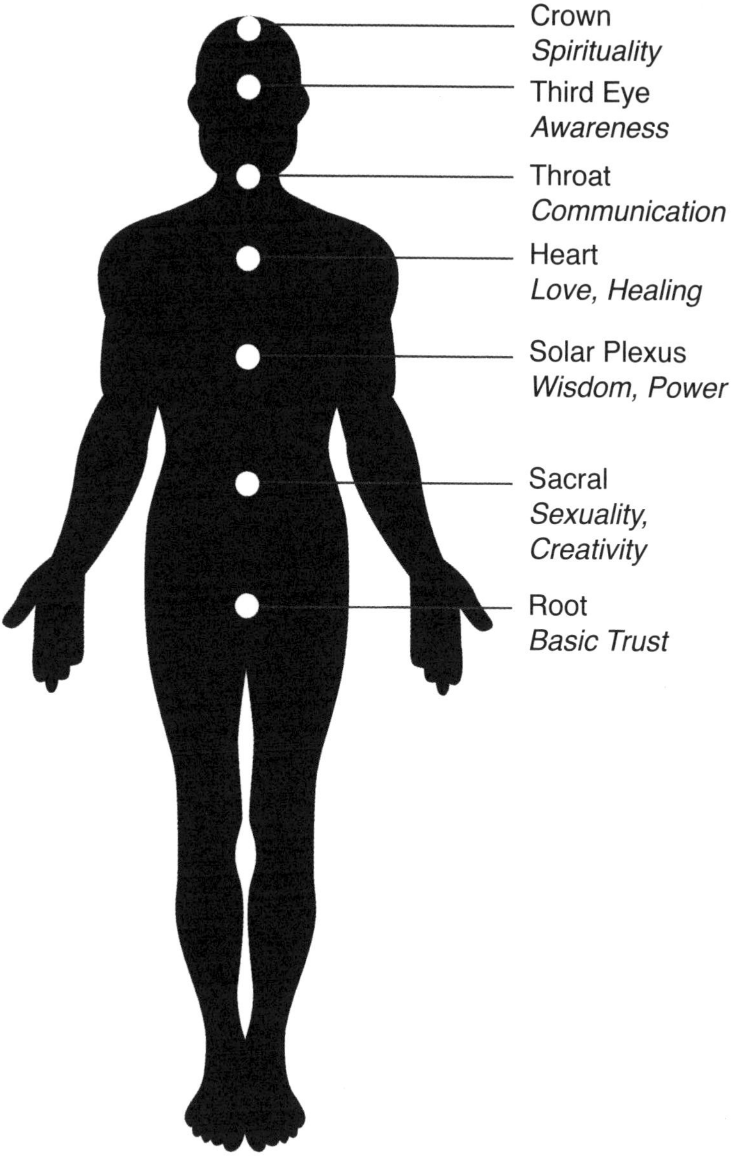
Crown
Spirituality
Third Eye
Awareness
Throat
Communication
Heart
Love, Healing
Solar Plexus
Wisdom, Power
Sacral
Sexuality, Creativity
Root
Basic Trust

NOTES, THOUGHTS, IDEAS:

ENERGY AND THOUGHTS

Read Chapter 3, pp. 22-25 of *Conquering Toxic Emotions* before completing this section.

OILY SUGGESTIONS: Apply Idaho Blue Spruce or Frankincense on the crown of the head, and inhale deeply.

Light energy makes up ___________ of the body's atoms and cells.

According to the Bible, thoughts have ___________ power.

As you choose good ___________, which have positive vibrations or ___________, you attract more of the same. This is known as the ______________________.

Sometimes after an uncomfortable situation, I will replay the scene over and over in my mind, thinking about what I could have said. Each time I replay it, the negativity of the situation becomes stronger. By replaying it time and time again, I am giving it more and more negative energy.

Note the thoughts that have replayed in your mind over the last 24 hours:

____

____

____

____

Your ___________ are an internal ___________ system.

Your ___________ are gifts that enable you to evaluate your ___________ life.

Take a look at yourself in the mirror and describe what you see:

____

____

____

____

There was a time when I would look in the mirror and all I could see were my imperfections – dark circles around my eyes, a nose that is too big, the wrong color of eyes, imperfect posture and so on. I was very critical of myself and felt badly each time I looked at myself.

Proverbs 23:7 says, "For as he thinks in his heart, so he is."

Your ___________ mind is logical: it reasons; performs ___________ thinking; formulates ___________. It is our will.

Negative thinking can lead your mind into ___________ thinking, which has a serious effect on your ___________.

NOTES, THOUGHTS, IDEAS:

TOXIC THOUGHTS

Read Chapter 4, pp. 26-27 of *Conquering Toxic Emotions* before completing this section.

OILY SUGGESTIONS: Apply Release™, Surrender™ or Bergamot over the heart, and inhale deeply.

__________ thinking will lead to toxic thinking, which may lead to sickness, __________ and death.

Science tells us __________ thoughts are __________ in your mind as well as in the __________ of your body.

Take a minute to record the last time you were ill or in pain, then think about your emotional state prior to that experience.

____

____

____

____

Typically, we experience negative emotions when we are under extra stress or worried about a situation.

How can you reframe your thoughts around that experience to upgrade them and possibly avoid the physical symptoms in the future?

____

____

____

____

By intentionally choosing to __________ your thoughts, you can __________ the course of your __________ and even your __________.

NOTES, THOUGHTS, IDEAS:

THOUGHTS AND WORDS

Read Chapter 5, pp. 28-31 of *Conquering Toxic Emotions* before completing this section.

OILY SUGGESTIONS: Apply Envision™, Believe™ or Cypress on pulse points, and inhale deeply.

Proverbs 19:21 says, "Death and life are in the power of the ___________."

Write down five phrases you often use.

____

____

____

____

____

If you are like most people, your list may include something like this: "that just kills me", "I thought I was going to die", "it just broke my heart", "burns my britches".

How can you upgrade your words to form positive confessions?

____

____

____

____

"Out of the ___________ of the heart his ___________ speaks." Luke 6:45

Negative thinking leads to ___________ thoughts.

The words that you ___________ have the ability to ___________ your environment with ___________, good or bad that will be stored in every ___________ of your body.

___________ are empowering, deliberate words that you may use to upgrade your ___________ and ___________ your mind.

Much of your ___________ is driven by your ___________ system.

NOTES, THOUGHTS, IDEAS:

SMELLS AND ESSENTIAL OILS

Read Chapter 6, pp. 32-37 of *Conquering Toxic Emotions* before completing this section.

OILY SUGGESTIONS: Apply Valor®, Grounding™ or Lavender across the top of the shoulders and on the bottom of the feet, and inhale deeply.

When I was a young girl, we spent Christmas at my Grandma's house. She always baked cinnamon rolls, and her house carried the wonderful aroma of baking bread and cinnamon. Because of this pleasant memory, whenever I smell cinnamon, it makes me happy!

Make a note of smells that you associate with specific memories and the emotions that accompany your experiences:

____

____

____

____

____

____

____

____

When you inhale a fragrance, the odor ____________ travel up your ____________ into the ____________ system of the ____________.

Pure, therapeutic-grade essential oils have been known to be some of the oldest agents in ___________ to have the ability to ___________ through our ___________ system.

Science teaches us that ___________ stimulates our ___________ first, and our rational ___________ second.

This is one of the reasons pure therapeutic ___________ oils are powerful in assisting the body to remain in ___________ or at homeostasis.

What are the five imperative components of choosing essential oils?

1) ____

2) ____

3) ____

4) ____

5) ____

List three specific ways to use essential oils for each category:

Topical:

1) ____

2) ____

3) ____

Aromatic:

1) ______________________________

2) ______________________________

3) ______________________________

Internal:

1) ______________________________

2) ______________________________

3) ______________________________

NOTES, THOUGHTS, IDEAS:

CLEARING NEGATIVE EMOTIONS

Read Chapter 7, pp. 38-40 of *Conquering Toxic Emotions* before completing this section.

OILY SUGGESTIONS: Apply Trauma Life™, SARA™, or Release™ around the navel, and inhale deeply.

2 Timothy 1:7 says, "God has not given us the spirit of fear, but power, love and a sound mind."

Our emotions are just a record of our past, and the good news is we can change our future!

Name the five thought processes to address prior to beginning your emotional detox:

1) ______________________________

2) ______________________________

3) ______________________________

4) ______________________________

5) ______________________________

Remember YOU are ___________ it!!

List the ten tips for a successful emotional detox:

1) ______________________________

2) ______________________________

3) ______________________________

4) ______________________________

5) ______________________________

6) ______________________________

7) ______________________________

8) ______________________________

9) ______________________________

10) ______________________________

NOTES, THOUGHTS, IDEAS:

TECHNIQUES TO ENHANCE EMOTIONAL WORK

Read Chapter 8, pp. 41-47 of *Conquering Toxic Emotions* before completing this section.

OILY SUGGESTIONS: Apply Motivation™, Inspiration™, Blue Cypress on temples and base of skull, and inhale deeply.

The addition of essential oils to these techniques synergizes the therapy, assisting to bring balance to the body.

The art of ___________ is based on the theory that points on the feet, hands, lower legs, ears and face correspond with different ___________ of the ___________.

As it is known today, ___________ found on the feet and ___________ follow the ___________ of the body.

Vita flex is a specialized form of digital ___________ that uses the pads and nails of the ___________ in a rolling motion to move ___________ (or electrical currents) through the body via ___________ points. (See p. 44 of *Conquering Toxic Emotions* for more information about Vita flex Technique.)

You may refer to the mapping of the feet on page 43 of *Conquering Toxic Emotions* to target specific areas of the body. Apply a drop or two of one or more essential oils prior to performing reflexology or Vita flex.

Auricular ___________ is a diagnostic and treatment system based on normalizing the body's ___________ by stimulating definite points on the ___________.

Studies and experience have revealed ___________ is effective in both the ___________ and ___________ realms.

Locate the auricular point for fear on the diagram on page 47 of *Conquering Toxic Emotions.*

NOTES, THOUGHTS, IDEAS:

EMOTIONS, OILS AND AFFIRMATIONS

Read Chapter 9, pp. 48-56 of *Conquering Toxic Emotions* before completing this section.

OILY SUGGESTIONS: Apply Abundance, Palo Santo or Orange over the ears, then inhale deeply.

By making very specific ___________, we take conscious ___________ of our ___________. The addition of ________________ aids to quickly release and change the ___________.

List four of the tips for using affirmations and oils.

1) ____

2) ____

3) ____

4) ____

NOTES, THOUGHTS, IDEAS:

BALANCING ENERGY CENTERS

Read Chapter 10, pp. 57-58 of *Conquering Toxic Emotions* before completing this section.

First, choose the Chakra or energy center you desire to focus on, and write down the corresponding affirmation and oil(s) you will be using to balance. Next, apply the oil at the suggested location on your body as you state your affirmation aloud several times.

Chakra:____

Affirmation: ____________________________________

Oil(s):____

Chakra:____

Affirmation: ____________________________________

Oil(s):____

Chakra:____

Affirmation: ____________________________________

Oil(s):____

Chakra:____

Affirmation: ____________________________________

Oil(s):____

Chakra:____

Affirmation: ____________________________________

Oil(s):____

Chakra:____

Affirmation: ____________________________________

Oil(s):____

Chakra:____

Affirmation: ____________________________________

Oil(s):____

Chakra:____

Affirmation: ____________________________________

Oil(s):____

Chakra:____

Affirmation: ____________________________________

Oil(s):____

Chakra:____

Affirmation: ____________________________________

Oil(s):____

EMOTIONAL CLEARING TECHNIQUE

Read Chapter 11, pp. 59-64 of *Conquering Toxic Emotions* before completing this section.

For your personal growth, a Gratitude – Goal Journal is included immediately following this section. You will likely find this so rewarding that you will choose to continue it beyond 30 days.

To obtain optimal results, follow all 10 Steps in the Emotional Clearing Technique on pp. 59-60.

In this section, you will record the emotions you have chosen to clear, along with the associated oils and affirmations. As you work through the process, you will track your progress of clearing or overcoming these emotional hindrances. Rewarding yourself once you have successfully eliminated a toxic emotion is well deserved and a great motivator.

Emotion: ______________________________

Oil:______________________________

Affirmation: ______________________________

Date Began Clearing: ______________________________

Date Successfully Eliminated:______________________________

Reward to myself:______________________________

Emotion: ______________________________________

Oil:____

Affirmation: ___________________________________

Date Began Clearing: ____________________________

Date Successfully Eliminated:_____________________

Reward to myself:________________________________

Emotion: ______________________________________

Oil:____

Affirmation: ___________________________________

Date Began Clearing: ____________________________

Date Successfully Eliminated:_____________________

Reward to myself:________________________________

Emotion: ______________________________________

Oil:____

Affirmation: ___________________________________

Date Began Clearing: ____________________________

Date Successfully Eliminated:_____________________

Reward to myself:________________________________

Emotion: ___________________________________

Oil: ___________________________________

Affirmation: ___________________________________

Date Began Clearing: ___________________________________

Date Successfully Eliminated: ___________________________________

Reward to myself: ___________________________________

Emotion: ___________________________________

Oil: ___________________________________

Affirmation: ___________________________________

Date Began Clearing: ___________________________________

Date Successfully Eliminated: ___________________________________

Reward to myself: ___________________________________

Emotion: ___________________________________

Oil: ___________________________________

Affirmation: ___________________________________

Date Began Clearing: ___________________________________

Date Successfully Eliminated: ___________________________________

Reward to myself: ___________________________________

Emotion: ______________________________

Oil:______________________________

Affirmation: ______________________________

Date Began Clearing: ______________________________

Date Successfully Eliminated:______________________________

Reward to myself:______________________________

Emotion: ______________________________

Oil:______________________________

Affirmation: ______________________________

Date Began Clearing: ______________________________

Date Successfully Eliminated:______________________________

Reward to myself:______________________________

Emotion: ______________________________

Oil:______________________________

Affirmation: ______________________________

Date Began Clearing: ______________________________

Date Successfully Eliminated:______________________________

Reward to myself:______________________________

Emotion: ____

Oil:____

Affirmation: _______________________________________

Date Began Clearing: ________________________________

Date Successfully Eliminated:__________________________

Reward to myself:___________________________________

Emotion: ____

Oil:____

Affirmation: _______________________________________

Date Began Clearing: ________________________________

Date Successfully Eliminated:__________________________

Reward to myself:___________________________________

Emotion: ____

Oil:____

Affirmation: _______________________________________

Date Began Clearing: ________________________________

Date Successfully Eliminated:__________________________

Reward to myself:___________________________________

GRATITUDE SELF-DISCOVERY JOURNAL

Journaling is a powerful tool to reduce stress, manage negative emotions, and enhance clarity. The act of writing down our dreams, goals, and action plans significantly increases our level of success in achieving them. This intentional act opens our subconscious to ideas and opportunities that are otherwise overlooked.

Gratitude is one of the most powerful experiences we can have. Gratitude goes beyond being thankful. It is a deep heart-felt appreciation. When we are in a state of gratitude, our lives are enriched and transformed on every level.

This section of the workbook allows you to explore and express your inner thoughts, desires and emotions, leading to personal growth and development on a very intimate level. This type of inner work is known to increase our ability to solve problems, increase self-esteem, and improve our mental health.

Sample journal entry:

I am so grateful for: *My family is healthy.*

To ensure today is great, I will: *Reach out to a friend*

My goal today is: *Self care: drink enough water, take my supplements, meditate for 15 minutes.*

Positive action step: *Call friend and take her out for lunch.*

The highlight of my day was: *Having lunch with my friend and being supportive.*

DAY 1

I am so grateful for: ________________________________

____

____

____

____

To ensure today is great, I will: ______________________

____

____

____

____

My goal today is: ________________________________

____

____

____

____

Positive action step: ____

____

____

____

____

The highlight of my day was: ____________________________________

____

____

____

____

"If you want to lift yourself up, lift up someone else."
—Booker T. Washington

DAY 2

I am so grateful for: ______________________________

____

____

____

____

To ensure today is great, I will: ______________________

____

____

____

____

My goal today is: ___________________________________

____

____

____

____

Positive action step: ____

____

____

____

____

The highlight of my day was: ______________________________

____

____

____

____

"Remember no one can make you feel inferior without your consent."
—Eleanor Roosevelt

DAY 3

I am so grateful for: ______________________________

____

____

____

____

To ensure today is great, I will: ______________________________

____

____

____

____

My goal today is: ______________________________

____

____

____

____

Positive action step: ______________________________

____

____

____

____

The highlight of my day was: _________________________

____

____

____

____

"The only person you are destined to become
is the person you decide to be."
—Ralph Waldo Emerson

DAY 4

I am so grateful for: ______________________________

____

____

____

____

To ensure today is great, I will: ______________________________

____

____

____

____

My goal today is: ______________________________

____

____

____

____

Positive action step: ____

____

____

____

____

The highlight of my day was: ____________________________________

____

____

____

____

"If you can dream it, you can do it."
—Walt Disney

DAY 5

I am so grateful for: ______________________________

____

____

____

____

To ensure today is great, I will: ____________________

____

____

____

____

My goal today is: ________________________________

____

____

____

____

Positive action step: ___________________________________

____

____

____

____

The highlight of my day was: ___________________________

____

____

____

____

"Whatever the mind of man can conceive and believe, it can achieve."
—Napoleon Hill

DAY 6

I am so grateful for: ______________________________

____

____

____

____

To ensure today is great, I will: ____________________

____

____

____

____

My goal today is: _________________________________

____

____

____

____

Positive action step: ______________________________

____

____

____

____

The highlight of my day was: _______________________

____

____

____

____

"The future belongs to those who believe
in the beauty of their dreams."
—Eleanor Roosevelt

DAY 7

I am so grateful for: ______________________________

____

____

____

____

To ensure today is great, I will: ______________________________

____

____

____

____

My goal today is: ______________________________

____

____

____

____

Positive action step: ______________________________

____

____

____

____

The highlight of my day was: _______________________

____

____

____

____

"Your attitude, not your aptitude, will determine your altitude."
—Zig Ziglar

DAY 8

I am so grateful for: ______________________________

____

____

____

____

To ensure today is great, I will: ______________________________

____

____

____

____

My goal today is: ______________________________

____

____

____

____

Positive action step: ____________________________________

____

____

____

____

The highlight of my day was: ____________________________

____

____

____

____

"There will be obstacles. There will be doubters. There will be mistakes. But with hard work, there are no limits."
—Michael Phelps

DAY 9

I am so grateful for: ______________________________

____

____

____

____

To ensure today is great, I will: ______________________

____

____

____

____

My goal today is: __________________________________

____

____

____

____

Positive action step: ______________________________

____

____

____

____

The highlight of my day was: ______________________

____

____

____

____

"Believe in yourself! Have faith in your abilities! Without a humble but reasonable confidence in your own powers you cannot be successful or happy."
—Norman Vincent Peale

DAY 10

I am so grateful for:

To ensure today is great, I will:

My goal today is:

Positive action step: ______________________________________

____

____

____

____

The highlight of my day was: ____________________________

____

____

____

____

"I've learned that people will forget what you said, people will forget what you did, but people will never forget how you made them feel."
—Maya Angelou

DAY 11

I am so grateful for: ______________________________

____

____

____

____

To ensure today is great, I will: ______________________________

____

____

____

____

My goal today is: ______________________________

____

____

____

____

Positive action step: ______________________________

____

____

____

____

The highlight of my day was: ______________________

____

____

____

____

"Start where you are. Use what you have. Do what you can."
—Arthur Ashe

DAY 12

I am so grateful for: ______________________________

____

____

____

____

To ensure today is great, I will: ______________________

____

____

____

____

My goal today is: ______________________________

____

____

____

____

Positive action step: ________________________________

____

____

____

____

The highlight of my day was: __________________________

____

____

____

____

"Creativity is intelligence having fun."
— Albert Einstein

DAY 13

I am so grateful for: ________________________________

____

____

____

____

To ensure today is great, I will: _______________________

____

____

____

____

My goal today is: __________________________________

____

____

____

____

Positive action step: ______________________________

____

____

____

____

The highlight of my day was: ______________________

____

____

____

____

"For as he thinks in his heart, so is he."
—Proverbs 23:7 NKJ

DAY 14

I am so grateful for: ______________________________

____

____

____

____

To ensure today is great, I will: ______________________________

____

____

____

____

My goal today is: ______________________________

____

____

____

____

Positive action step: ______________________________

____

____

____

____

The highlight of my day was: ______________________

____

____

____

____

"Never give up, for that is just the place and time that the tide will turn."
—Harriet Beecher Stow

DAY 15

I am so grateful for: ____________________________________

____

____

____

____

To ensure today is great, I will: _____________________________

____

____

____

____

My goal today is: ______________________________________

____

____

____

____

Positive action step: ______________________________

____

____

____

____

The highlight of my day was: ______________________

____

____

____

____

"Whether you think you can or think you can't, you're right."
—Henry Ford

DAY 16

I am so grateful for: ____________________________________

____

____

____

____

To ensure today is great, I will: __________________________

____

____

____

____

My goal today is: _______________________________________

____

____

____

____

Positive action step: ________________________________

____

____

____

____

The highlight of my day was: ___________________________

____

____

____

____

"Talent wins game, but teamwork wins championships."
—Michael Jordan

DAY 17

I am so grateful for: ______________________________

To ensure today is great, I will: ______________________

My goal today is: ______________________________

Positive action step: ______________________________

____

____

____

____

The highlight of my day was: ______________________

____

____

____

____

Change your thoughts and you change your world.
—Norman Vincent Peale

DAY 18

I am so grateful for: ________________________________

____

____

____

____

To ensure today is great, I will: ________________________

____

____

____

____

My goal today is: ________________________________

____

____

____

____

Positive action step: ______________________________

____

____

____

____

The highlight of my day was: _______________________

____

____

____

____

"Setting goals is the first step in turning the invisible into the visible."
—Tony Robbins

DAY 19

I am so grateful for: ______________________________

____

____

____

____

To ensure today is great, I will: ______________________________

____

____

____

____

My goal today is: ______________________________

____

____

____

____

Positive action step: ____________________________________

____

____

____

____

The highlight of my day was: ____________________________

____

____

____

____

"You are never too old to set a new goal or to dream a new dream."
—C.S. Lewis

DAY 20

I am so grateful for: ______________________________

____

____

____

____

To ensure today is great, I will: ____________________

____

____

____

____

My goal today is: ______________________________

____

____

____

____

Positive action step: ______________________________

____

____

____

____

The highlight of my day was: ________________________

____

____

____

____

"The people who are crazy enough to think they
can change the world are the ones who do."
—Steve Jobs

DAY 21

I am so grateful for: ______________________________

____

____

____

____

To ensure today is great, I will: ______________________

____

____

____

____

My goal today is: ____________________________

____

____

____

____

Positive action step: ______________________________

____

____

____

____

The highlight of my day was: _______________________

____

____

____

____

"I have not failed. I've just found 10,000 ways that won't work."
—Thomas Edison

DAY 22

I am so grateful for: ______________________________

____

____

____

____

To ensure today is great, I will: ______________________

____

____

____

____

My goal today is: ______________________________

____

____

____

____

Positive action step: ______________________________

____

____

____

____

The highlight of my day was: ______________________

____

____

____

____

"Obstacles are those frightful things you see
when you take your eyes off your goal."
—Henry Ford

DAY 23

I am so grateful for: ______________________________

____

____

____

____

To ensure today is great, I will: ______________________________

____

____

____

____

My goal today is: ______________________________

____

____

____

____

Positive action step: ____________________________________

____

____

____

____

The highlight of my day was: ______________________________

____

____

____

____

"Either you run the day, or the day runs you."
—Jim Rohn

DAY 24

I am so grateful for: ______________________________

____

____

____

____

To ensure today is great, I will: ________________________

____

____

____

____

My goal today is: _______________________________

____

____

____

____

Positive action step: ____

____

____

____

____

The highlight of my day was: _______________________________

____

____

____

____

"The difference between a successful person and others is not lack of strength, not a lack of knowledge, but rather a lack of will."
—Vince Lombardi

DAY 25

I am so grateful for: ______

To ensure today is great, I will: ______

My goal today is: ______

Positive action step: ______________________________

____

____

____

____

The highlight of my day was: ________________________

____

____

____

____

"Don't worry about failures, worry about the chances you miss when you don't even try."
—Jack Canfield

DAY 26

I am so grateful for: ______________________________

____

____

____

____

To ensure today is great, I will: ______________________________

____

____

____

____

My goal today is: ______________________________

____

____

____

____

Positive action step: ______________________________

____

____

____

____

The highlight of my day was: ______________________

____

____

____

____

"Many of life's failures are experienced by people who did not realize how close they were to success when they gave up."
—Thomas Edison

DAY 27

I am so grateful for: ______________________________

____

____

____

____

To ensure today is great, I will: ______________________

____

____

____

____

My goal today is: _________________________________

____

____

____

____

Positive action step: ______________________________

____

____

____

____

The highlight of my day was: ______________________

____

____

____

____

"Every strike brings me closer to the next home run."
—Babe Ruth

DAY 28

I am so grateful for: ________________________________

____

____

____

____

To ensure today is great, I will: ________________________

____

____

____

____

My goal today is: ______________________________

____

____

____

____

Positive action step: ____________________________________

____

____

____

____

The highlight of my day was: ______________________________

____

____

____

____

"Keep away from people who try to belittle your ambitions. Small people always do that, but the really great make you feel that you, too, can become great."
—Mark Twain

DAY 29

I am so grateful for: ______________________________

____

____

____

____

To ensure today is great, I will: ____________________

____

____

____

____

My goal today is: __________________________________

____

____

____

____

Positive action step: ______________________________

____

____

____

____

The highlight of my day was: ____________________

____

____

____

____

"We become what we think about."
—Earl Nightingale

DAY 30

I am so grateful for: ____________________

To ensure today is great, I will: ____________________

My goal today is: ____________________

Positive action step: ______________________________

____

____

____

____

The highlight of my day was: ______________________

____

____

____

____

"Failure will never overtake me if my determination to succeed is strong enough."
—Og Mandino

NOTES

NOTES

NOTES

POSITIVE ACTION STEPS

To further enhance your day and that of those around you, complete one positive action step per day. You may choose your own or use one of these suggestions.

Send a hand written note.

Do something you enjoy everyday.

Edify someone.

Pay the tab for the person behind you.

Learn to say no with grace and ease.

Thank someone for something they did in the past.

Compliment a stranger.

Make an effort to go outside everyday.

Smile at everyone you see.

Send a care package to someone.

Encourage someone.

Allow someone to go in front of you at checkout.

Stop multitasking, and savor the task at hand.

Offer to babysit for a friend so they can have a date night.

Give a gift card to someone that is a blessing to you.

Accept your compliments. Don't deflect or minimize them.

Mail a card to a friend you haven't heard from in a while.

Send flowers to a business that provides a service to you.

Unplug for an hour.

Volunteer at a homeless shelter.

Go outside and get 15 minutes of sun.

Leave money in a vending machine.

Take a quick nap.

Bake cookies and bring to a nursing home.

Serve your spouse breakfast in bed.

Hold the door for someone.

Make an uplifting social media post.

Send coloring books and crayons to a children's hospital.

Pick up trash at your local park.

Relax in an essential oil bath.

Have coffee with a friend.

Mow your neighbor's lawn.

Bring goodies to share to work.

Volunteer at a youth center.

Tell someone all the things you love about them.

Call your grandparents.

Call someone you haven't talked to in a while.

Bring the crossing guard a cup of coffee.

Donate your previously read books to the library.

Take a "me" day.

Buy yourself a gift.

Clean out a closet or cabinet, and donate what you aren't using to charity.

Make a special dessert for a neighbor.

Listen to your favorite music for 15 minutes.

Run an errand for a new mom or a sick friend.

THE GOALS I CHOOSE TO ACHIEVE

As you proceed through this journey of self-discovery, self-improvement and inner healing, you will find that you are inspired to set goals and take action to achieve them. It is very rewarding to track your progress and accomplishments, and you may use this section for that purpose.

Date: ______________________________

Goal: ______________________________

Action Plan: ______________________________

Completed: ______________________________

Date: ______________________________

Goal: ______________________________

Action Plan: ______________________________

Completed: ______________________________

Date: ______________________________

Goal: ______________________________

Action Plan: ______________________________

Completed: ______________________________

Date: ______________________________

Goal: ______________________________

Action Plan: ________________________

Completed: _________________________

Date: ______________________________

Goal: ______________________________

Action Plan: ________________________

Completed: _________________________

Date: ______________________________

Goal: ______________________________

Action Plan: ________________________

Completed: _________________________

Date: ______________________________

Goal: ______________________________

Action Plan: ________________________

Completed: _________________________

Date: ____

Goal: ____

Action Plan: ______________________________________

Completed: _______________________________________

Date: ____

Goal: ____

Action Plan: ______________________________________

Completed: _______________________________________

Date: ____

Goal: ____

Action Plan: ______________________________________

Completed: _______________________________________

Date: ____

Goal: ____

Action Plan: ______________________________________

Completed: _______________________________________

Date: ____

Goal: ____

Action Plan: ____

Completed: ____

Date: ____

Goal: ____

Action Plan: ____

Completed: ____

Date: ____

Goal: ____

Action Plan: ____

Completed: ____

Date: ____

Goal: ____

Action Plan: ____

Completed: ____

Date: ______________________________

Goal: ______________________________

Action Plan: ______________________________

Completed: ______________________________

Date: ______________________________

Goal: ______________________________

Action Plan: ______________________________

Completed: ______________________________

Date: ______________________________

Goal: ______________________________

Action Plan: ______________________________

Completed: ______________________________

Date: ______________________________

Goal: ______________________________

Action Plan: ______________________________

Completed: ______________________________

EMOTIONAL QUESTIONNAIRES

Read Chapter 12, pp. 65-79 of *Conquering Toxic Emotions* while completing this section.

This section will help guide you through the Emotional Questionnaires. If you answer yes to the majority of the questions within a Questionnaire, this is an area you should consider clearing.

After determining which question you will work on, review the accompanying emotions, and locate the emotion(s) in the **Emotions, Oils and Affirmations** section (pp. 48-56) to determine an applicable affirmation. Record the applicable oil, emotion and affirmation. You are now ready to follow the 10 steps in the **Emotional Clearing Technique** section (pp. 59-60).

Questionnaire #1

1) ______________________________

2) ______________________________

3) ______________________________

4) ______________________________

Oil: ____________________ Emotion: ____________________

Affirmation: ______________________________

Questionnaire #2

1) ______________________________

2) ______________________________

3) ______________________________

4) ______________________________

5) ______________________________

Oil: ______________ Emotion: ______________

Affirmation: ______________________________

Questionnaire #3

1) ______________________________

2) ______________________________

3) ______________________________

Oil: ______________ Emotion: ______________

Affirmation: ______________________________

Questionnaire #4

1) ______________________________

2) ______________________________

3) ______________________________

4) ______________________________

Oil: ______________ Emotion: ______________

Affirmation: ______________________________

Questionnaire #5

1) ______________________________

2) ______________________________

3) ______________________________

4) ______________________________

Oil: ______________ Emotion: ______________

Affirmation: ______________________________

Questionnaire #6

1) ______________________________

2) ______________________________

3) ______________________________

4) ______________________________

Oil: ______________ Emotion: ______________

Affirmation: ______________________________

Questionnaire #7

1) ______________________________

2) ______________________________

3) ______________________________

4) ____

5) ____

Oil: ____________________ Emotion: ____________________

Affirmation: ____________________________________

Questionnaire #8

1) ____

2) ____

3) ____

4) ____

Oil: ____________________ Emotion: ____________________

Affirmation: ____________________________________

Questionnaire #9

1) ____

2) ____

3) ____

4) ____

Oil: ____________________ Emotion: ____________________

Affirmation: ____________________________________

Questionnaire #10

1) ____________________

2) ____________________

3) ____________________

4) ____________________

Oil: ____________ Emotion: ____________

Affirmation: ____________________

Questionnaire #11

1) ____________________

2) ____________________

3) ____________________

Oil: ____________ Emotion: ____________

Affirmation: ____________________

Questionnaire #12

1) ____________________

2) ____________________

3) ____________________

4) ____________________

5) ____________________

Oil: ____________ Emotion: ____________

Affirmation: ____________________

Questionnaire #13

1) ______________________________

2) ______________________________

3) ______________________________

4) ______________________________

5) ______________________________

Oil: ______________ Emotion: ______________

Affirmation: ______________________________

Questionnaire #14

1) ______________________________

2) ______________________________

3) ______________________________

Oil: ______________ Emotion: ______________

Affirmation: ______________________________

Questionnaire #15

1) ______________________________

2) ______________________________

3) ______________________________

4) ______________________________

Oil: ______________ Emotion: ______________

Affirmation: ______________________________

Questionnaire #16

1) ______________________________

2) ______________________________

3) ______________________________

4) ______________________________

Oil: ______________ Emotion: ______________

Affirmation: ______________________________

Questionnaire #17

1) ______________________________

2) ______________________________

3) ______________________________

4) ______________________________

Oil: ______________ Emotion: ______________

Affirmation: ______________________________

Questionnaire #18

1) ______________________________

2) ______________________________

3) ______________________________

Oil: ______________ Emotion: ______________

Affirmation: ______________________________

Questionnaire #19

1) ______________________________

2) ______________________________

3) ______________________________

Oil: ______________ Emotion: ______________

Affirmation: ______________________________

Questionnaire #20

1) ______________________________

2) ______________________________

3) ______________________________

4) ______________________________

Oil: ______________ Emotion: ______________

Affirmation: ______________________________

Questionnaire #21

1) ______________________________

2) ______________________________

3) ______________________________

Oil: ______________ Emotion: ______________

Affirmation: ______________________________

Questionnaire #22

1) ____

2) ____

3) ____

Oil: ____________________ Emotion: ____________________

Affirmation: ______________________________________

Questionnaire #23

1) ____

2) ____

3) ____

4) ____

5) ____

Oil: ____________________ Emotion: ____________________

Affirmation: ______________________________________

Questionnaire #24

1) ____

2) ____

3) ____

Oil: ____________________ Emotion: ____________________

Affirmation: ______________________________________

Questionnaire #25

1) ____________________

2) ____________________

Oil: __________ Emotion: __________

Affirmation: ____________________

Questionnaire #26

1) ____________________

2) ____________________

3) ____________________

Oil: __________ Emotion: __________

Affirmation: ____________________

Questionnaire #27

1) ____________________

2) ____________________

3) ____________________

4) ____________________

5) ____________________

Oil: __________ Emotion: __________

Affirmation: ____________________

FINAL WORDS FROM THE AUTHOR

Learn to love yourself. Loving yourself greatly enhances the body's ability to heal and remain healthy. Learn to forgive yourself. Forgiveness is a gift to ourselves that frees us to be who we were created to be. It is impossible for us to give to others something we don't have, so we must learn to love, forgive and intentionally choose to be grateful and content in whatever situation we find ourselves. No, we can't control everything that happens, but we can control how we respond.

My prayer is that you have found emotional freedom, which leads to optimal health, peace, and contentment. The success of our life isn't measured by how many things we accumulate, the size of our bank account, or the number of friends we have. Life is about our experiences; it is about having fun and blessing others. I believe in paying it forward because I know I can never out give God or the universe, and what I put out returns to me.

I choose to be a WORLD CHANGER and challenge you to be a WORLD CHANGER, too!

Make your life amazing!

Rhonda

To obtain additional copies and for more information on other books by Growing Healthy Homes, please visit our website at www.GrowingHealthyHomes.com

Conquering Toxic Emotions

Gentle Babies

Nutrition 101: Choose Life!

Essentials: 50 Answers to Common Questions about Essential Oils

The ABC's of Building a Young Living Organization